READING
SATs TESTS
YEAR 6

SCHOLASTIC

Scholastic Education, an imprint of Scholastic Ltd
Book End, Range Road, Witney, Oxfordshire, OX29 0YD
Registered office: Westfield Road, Southam,
Warwickshire CV47 0RA

www.scholastic.co.uk

© 2019 Scholastic Ltd

23456789 8901234567

A British Library Cataloguing-in-Publication Data
A catalogue record for this book is available from the British
Library.

ISBN 978-1407-18307-7
Printed and bound by Ashford Colour Press

Author
Graham Fletcher

Series consultants
Lesley and Graham Fletcher

Editorial team
Rachel Morgan, Tracey Cowell, Anna Hall,
Rebecca Rothwell, Shelley Welsh and Sally Rigg

Design team
Nicolle Thomas, Alice Duggan
and Oxford Designers and Illustrators

Cover illustrations
Istock/calvindexter and Tomek.gr / Shutterstock/Visual Generation

Acknowledgements
Extracts from Department for Education website © Crown Copyright. Reproduced under the terms of the Open Government Licence
(OGL). www.nationalarchives.gov.uk/doc/open-government-licence/version/3/

The publishers gratefully acknowledge permission to reproduce the following copyright material:
Graham Fletcher for the use of 'A handbook for wolves', 'Visiting England', Into the Underworld, 'Modern-day pirates', 'The best
Christmas ever' 'Japan' and 'Reaching Treasure Island'. Text © 2015, Graham Fletcher.
Pollinger Ltd for the use of 'Snake' from The Complete Poems of D.H. Lawrence reprinted by permission of Pollinger Limited (www.
pollingerltd.com) on behalf of the Estate of Frieda Lawrence Ravagli.
Every effort has been made to trace copyright holders for the works reproduced in this publication, and the publishers apologise for
any inadvertent omissions.

Illustrations: Moreno Chiacchiera, Beehive Illustration and Tomek.gr
Photographs:
Test A: © Paul Daniels/Shutterstock; © Barnes Ian/Shutterstock; © Matthew Dixon/Shutterstock; © Shanna Hyatt/Shutterstock;
        © Lakov Kalinin/Shutterstock; © Gwoeii/Shutterstock; © r.nagy/Shutterstock
Test B: REX/Snap Stills
Test C: © Haveseen/Shutterstock; © Bozena Fulawka/Shutterstock; © Dusan002/Shutterstock; © Golbay/Shutterstock

Contents
Reading: Year 6

Contents	Page
Introduction	

| **Tests** | |

| **Marks & guidance** | |

About this book

This book provides you with practice papers to help support children with the Key Stage 2 Reading test and to assess which skills need further development.

Using the practice papers

The practice papers in this book can be used as you would any other practice materials. The children will need to be familiar with specific test-focused skills, such as reading carefully, leaving questions until the end if they seem too difficult, working at a suitable pace and checking through their work.

If you choose to use the papers for looking at content rather than practising tests, do be aware of the time factor. The tests require a lot of work to be done in 1 hour as they are testing the degree of competence children have – it is not enough to be able to answer questions correctly but slowly.

About the tests

Each Reading test consists of texts covering different genres and contains 50 marks. Each test lasts for 1 hour, including reading time.

- Reading texts: children may underline, highlight or make notes.
- Questions: children should refer back to the reading texts for their answers.

The marks available for each question are shown in the test paper next to each question and are also shown next to each answer in the mark scheme. Incorrect answers do not get a mark and no half marks should be given.

There are three different types of answer:

- **Selected answers**: children may be required to choose an option from a list; draw lines to match answers; or tick a correct answer. Usually 1 mark will be awarded.
- **Short answers**: children will need to write a phrase or use information from the text. Usually 1–2 marks will be awarded.
- **Several line answers**: children will need to write a sentence or two. Usually 1–2 marks will be awarded.
- **Longer answers**: children will usually need to write more than one sentence using information from the text. Up to 3 marks will be awarded.

Advice for parents and carers

How this book will help

This book will support your child to get ready for the KS2 National Reading tests commonly called SATs. It provides valuable practice and help on the responses and content expected of Year 6 children aged 10–11 years.

In the weeks (and sometimes months) leading up to the National Tests, your child will be given plenty of practice, revision and tips to give them the best possible chance to demonstrate their knowledge and understanding. It is important to try to practise outside of school and many children benefit from extra input. This book will help your child prepare further and build their confidence and their ability to work to a time limit. Practice is vital and every opportunity helps, so don't start too late.

In this book you will find three Reading tests. The layout and format of each test closely matches those used in the National Tests, so your child will become familiar with what to expect and get used to the style of the tests. There is a comprehensive answer section and guidance about how to mark the questions.

Tips

- Make sure that you allow your child to take the test in a quiet environment where they are not likely to be interrupted or distracted.
- Make sure your child has a flat surface to work on with plenty of space to spread out and good light.
- Emphasise the importance of reading and re-reading a question and to underline or circle any important information.
- These papers are similar to the one your child will take in May in Year 6 and they therefore give you a good idea of strengths and areas for development. So, when you have found areas that require some more practice, it is useful to go over these again and practise similar types of question with your child.
- Go through the tests again together, identify any gaps in learning and address any misconceptions or areas of misunderstanding. If you are unsure of anything yourself, then make an appointment to see your child's teacher who will be able to help and advise further.

Advice for children

What to do before the test

- Revise and practise on a regular basis.
- Spend some time each week practising.
- Focus on the areas you are least confident in to get better.
- Get a good night's sleep and eat a wholesome breakfast.
- Be on time for school.
- Have all the necessary materials.
- Avoid stressful situations before a test.

What to do in the test

- The test is 60 minutes long. You should allow time to read the texts and then answer the questions.
- Read one text and then answer the questions about that text before moving on to read the next text.
- You may highlight, underline or make notes on the texts.
- There are 50 marks. The marks for each question are shown in the margin on the right of each page.
- Make sure you read the instructions carefully. There are different types of answer.
  - Short answers: have a short line or box. This shows that you need only write a word or a few words in your answer.
  - Several line answers: have a few lines. This gives you space to write more words or a sentence or two.
  - Longer answers: have lots of lines. This shows that a longer, more detailed answer is needed. You can write in full sentences if you want to.
  - Selected answers: for these questions, you do not need to write anything at all and you should tick, draw lines to, or put a ring around your answer. Read the instructions carefully so that you know how to answer the question.

Test coverage

Children will need to be able to:

- Give and explain meanings of words.
- Find and copy key details.
- Summarise main ideas from more than one paragraph.
- Use details from the texts to explain their thoughts about them.
- Predict what might happen.
- Identify and explain how information is organised.
- Show how writers use language to create an effect.
- Make comparisons.

Test A

A HANDBOOK FOR WOLVES

Emergency in Wolf World!

While you are reading this, check over your shoulder, little wolves. Is there anything behind you? Is it pink? Is it pig-shaped?

Yes? Run!
No? Read on.

Yesterday, in broad daylight, without provocation, one of our most respected wolves was lured into the home of three pigs and brutally murdered! The Three Little Pigs are now Public Enemy Number One in Wolf World. They may look little; they may look harmless; but these little piggies are the real deal. They are so dangerous that you should give them a wide berth.

Help is at hand

All is not lost, little brothers. You are all in danger and in fear for your lives. However, do not worry. There is no need to have nightmares. We have written a survival manual just in case you run into these baby-faced monsters.

STEP 1

If possible, avoid contact with any kind of pig. However, if this is not possible, run away at once as far as you can.

STEP 2

Check the fabric of your house. If it is made of straw or sticks, run as fast as you can to one of your friend's houses and hide there.

STEP 3

Hide! If the pigs follow you, put a big pan of water on the fire to boil.

STEP 4

Shout through the letter box that the only way they'll ever get you is to come down the chimney.

STEP 5

Watch the pig-shaped shadows climb up on the roof. Listen to the scratching at the top of the chimney. Feel terrified, then… sit back and enjoy!

Is that it?

Yes, it's as simple as that. Pigs are stupid animals. They're bound to fall for your trick.

Remember: Don't take risks. Butter wouldn't melt in their mouths but wolves will in their pot!

VISITING

England

For over fifty years, we have been flocking to the sun-kissed beaches of Spain, Italy and Greece. The English tourist industry has suffered as a result of this. However, rising prices and lower pay rises are affecting family budgets and making foreign holidays less affordable. Perhaps now things could be changing. Perhaps now is the time to look at what is available nearer home. Perhaps now is the time for visiting England.

England. Yes, England: that 'green and pleasant land'. It's on our doorsteps, yet how many of us bother to see what this country has to offer?

▶ What can you do?

Let's start by considering what you like to do. Immediately, many people will say, 'Spend the day on a beach'. You don't need to go abroad for that. England has beaches to rival anything abroad and

you don't have to travel far to find them. Nowhere in England is more than 75 miles from the sea.

In the north-west there is big, brash Blackpool and the more sedate Southport. Both of these have wide expanses of golden sand, amusement arcades and large-scale rides for thrill seekers. On the east coast, Scarborough and Great Yarmouth are tourist magnets but if you like the pace of life a little slower, the crowds smaller and the atmosphere quieter, try Cromer, Filey or the romantically named Robin Hood's Bay. Further south you'll find the major tourist towns of Brighton and Bournemouth with sun during the day and exciting nightlife as well.

▶ But I don't want to go to the beach

If you are a lover of scenery, England has it in abundance. Its National Parks like Dartmoor, Exmoor, the Yorkshire Dales and the Peak District are famous throughout the world. The most impressive of all surely is the Lake District. This small area of land is packed with mountains and magnificent views, yet is it easily accessible with the M6 motorway leading visitors straight to it. This is the land of Beatrix Potter and William Wordsworth where, despite the numbers that visit each year, it is still possible to wander 'lonely as a cloud' and find peace and solitude. With all of the mountainous scenery, it is almost possible to forget the lakes themselves: Coniston, Ullswater and Windermere are just as beautiful as the hills that surround them and are thought by many to create the perfect scenic combination through the contrast of hills and water. Most people prefer to go to the Lake District in the summer when the weather is better, but for some hardy souls the winter is the time to go, when the snow falls, hiding the hills and creating picture-postcard Christmas scenes.

▶ But I don't want to go that far north

It is true that England's highest hills are in the north but there are other areas of outstanding natural beauty throughout the country. The Cotswolds are a range of rolling hills further south. Nestling among them are chocolate-box villages that seem to have come straight out of history. They are exactly what people think of when they picture English villages. Some of them have romantic, almost ancient names like Bourton-on-the-Water, conjuring up images of days gone by. Who could resist the mysteries suggested by the Slaughters, twin villages with a gruesome name?

▶ But I don't like looking at the scenery

It's quite possible that you aren't the sit-and-look type. Perhaps you want to do things instead, in which case, there are plenty of places for adventure. If you are after thrills, you could experience motor racing at places like Silverstone and Castle Donnington. Here you can choose from a nerve-tingling ride in a souped-up supercar or driving a single-seater lean machine while dreaming of being the next Lewis Hamilton. Don't dream too much though: the bends are very tricky!

If that's too fast for you, try caving in the Forest of Dean or Devon; riding in places as far apart as Cornwall and Cheshire; and fishing almost everywhere there is water.

▶ Is that all?

There are lots of choices to make. You could take a city break. York and Chester have really interesting Tudor streets. Take a walk down The Shambles and see what life used to be like.

London is worth a week by itself. Everything you've ever seen on television is there and it looks just like it does on the small screen, only much bigger. Buckingham Palace and the Houses of Parliament are musts. So is Trafalgar Square, guarded by its sentinel, Nelson, who in turn is protected by the lions at the bottom of his column. Wembley Stadium, the Tower of London, Westminster Abbey – the list just goes on and on. The West End with its spectacular shows. The Tube (London Underground), an unusual experience for most visitors but a way of life to Londoners. There's so much there that you might not see it all.

▶ What's the catch?

It all sounds too good to be true, doesn't it? So, is there a catch? No. There are only three possible downsides:

1. The weather. However, you live here so you are used to it. It never rains for long and there are lots of things to do indoors while you are waiting for it to stop.

2. The traffic. Sometimes it can take a while to get to places but don't be put off, the wait will be well worth it.

3. The amount of things to do and places to go. You won't be able to do everything so you'll have to choose and that won't be easy!

▶ But I don't want to go on holiday in England

Clearly this is the time for visiting England but if all this isn't enough for you and you still yearn for a little 'foreign' excitement, you could always try Wales or Scotland instead!

A London cab horse

This passage is about a horse called Black Beauty.

My new master's name was Jeremiah Barker, but as everyone called him Jerry, I shall do the same. Jerry had a cab of his own and two horses which he drove and attended to himself. His other horse was a tall, white, rather large-boned animal, called Captain; he was old now but when he was young he must have been splendid; he still had a proud way of holding his head and arching his neck; in fact, he was a high-bred, fine-mannered, noble old horse, every inch of him. He told me that in his early youth he went to the Crimean War; he belonged to an officer in the cavalry and used to lead the regiment.

Jerry's family were very kind to me. His wife, Polly, brought me a slice of apple each morning and his daughter, Dolly, brought me a piece of bread and made as much of me as if I had been the "Black Beauty" of olden times. It was a great treat to be petted again and talked to in a gentle voice, and I let them see as well as I could that I wished to be very friendly. Polly thought I was very handsome and a great deal too good for a cab, if it was not for the broken knees.

The first week of my life as a cab horse was very trying; I had never been used to London, and the noise, the hurry, the crowds of horses, carts and carriages that I had to make my way through made me feel anxious and harassed; but I soon found that I could perfectly trust Jerry, and then I got used to it. Captain would go out with the cab in the mornings and I would pull it in the afternoons.

Jerry was as good a driver as I had ever known; and, what was better, he took as much thought for his horses as he did for himself. He soon found out that I was willing to work and he never laid the whip on me unless it was gently drawing the end of it over my back when I was to go on; but generally I knew this quite well by the way in which he took up the reins; and I believe his whip was more frequently stuck up by his side than in his hand.

In a short time my master and I understood each other as well as a horse and man can do. In the stable too he did all that he could for our comfort. The stalls were the old-fashioned style, too much on the slope; but he had two movable bars fixed across the back of our stalls, so that at night and when we were resting he just took off our halters and put up the bars, and thus we could turn about and stand in whichever way we pleased, which was a great comfort.

Jerry kept us very clean, and gave us as much change of food as he could and always plenty of it; and not only that, but he always gave us plenty of clean water, which he allowed to stand by us both night and day; except, of course, when we came in warm. Some people say that a horse ought not to drink all he likes; but I know if we are allowed to drink when we want it, we drink only a little at a time, and it does us a great deal more good than swallowing down half a bucketful at a time, because we have been left without till we are thirsty and miserable. Some grooms will go home to their beer and leave us for hours with our dry hay and oats and nothing to moisten them; then, of course, we gulp down too much at once, which helps to spoil our breathing and sometimes chills our stomachs. But the best thing that we had was our Sundays for rest; we worked so hard in the week that I do not think we could have kept up to it but for that day; besides, we then had time to enjoy each other's company. It was on these days that I learned Captain's life story.

Adapted from *Black Beauty* by Anna Sewell

Marks

> **Questions** 1–13 are about *A handbook for wolves* on pages **8–9**.

1. This article is written for:

Tick **one**.

little pigs. ☐   little wolves. ☐

little readers. ☐   little chefs. ☐

1

2. Read the first line. What effect does the use of *you* and *your* have on the reader?

_____

_____

1

3.

> *Yesterday, in broad daylight, **without provocation**, one of our most respected wolves was lured into the home of three pigs and brutally murdered!*

How does *without provocation* make the reader feel sympathy for the wolf?

_____

_____

1

Marks

4.

> *The Three Little Pigs are now **Public Enemy Number One** in Wolf World.*

What does *Public Enemy Number One* mean in this sentence? Circle **one**.

The best criminals   The most wanted criminals

The most popular criminals   The first criminals

1

5.

> *They are so dangerous that you should give them a **wide berth**.*

What do the words *wide berth* tell the reader about what the wolves should do? Name **two** things.

1. _____

2. _____

2

6. Why is there no need for the wolves *to have nightmares*?

Tick **one**.

The pigs are harmless. ☐

The wolves will never run into the pigs. ☐

A survival manual has been written. ☐

The pigs are baby-faced. ☐

1

7.

> *We have written a survival manual just in case you run into these* **baby-faced monsters***.*

How do the words *baby-faced monsters* make you feel about the pigs?

_____

_____

Marks

1

8. Read **Step 1**.

Give **two** pieces of advice that this step gives to wolves about how to deal with pigs.

1. _____

2. _____

2

9. Read **Step 2**.

Find and **copy two** things that could be part of the fabric of a house.

1. _____

2. _____

2

10.

> *Feel terrified, then... sit back and enjoy!*

What does this instruction suggest is likely to happen next?

_____

_____

2

11. Read the opening paragraph and the final paragraph. How is the reader meant to feel at these parts of the story? Circle **one**.

Marks

happy at the beginning; frightened at the end

frightened at the beginning; happy at the end

frightened at the beginning; not bothered at the end

happy at the beginning; happy at the end

1

12. How does the information in the survival manual help the wolves?

_____

_____

_____

2

13. Throughout the story, the pigs are shown to be:

Tick **two**.

frightened. ⬜

dangerous. ⬜

untrustworthy. ⬜

threatened. ⬜

1

Marks

> **Questions** 14–24 are about *Visiting England* on pages 10–11.

14. For how long has the English tourist industry been suffering from foreign competition?

_____

1

15. Which word in the following sentence shows that it is an opinion?

> *Perhaps now things could be changing.*

_____

1

16. How far is the furthest place in England away from the sea?

_____

1

17. Put a tick in the correct box to show whether each of the following statements is a **fact** or **opinion**.

Marks

	Fact	Opinion
Blackpool and Southport are both in the north-west.		
Blackpool is big and brash.		
Southport is more sedate.		
Blackpool and Southport both have wide expanses of golden sand.		

1

18. The writer says that the Lake District is the *most impressive* of the National Parks. Tick **two** reasons that people might want to visit it.

Tick **two**.

It is in the south of England. ☐

It is packed with mountains and magnificent views. ☐

It has beaches and sea views. ☐

It has picture-postcard Christmas scenes. ☐

It can all be seen in one day. ☐

2

19.

> *...the winter is the time to go, when the snow falls, hiding the hills and creating picture-postcard Christmas scenes.*

This extract contains:

Tick **one**.

a simile. ☐

personification. ☐

alliteration. ☐

assonance. ☐

1

20. Read the section headed ***But I don't want to go that far north***.

Find and **copy one** sentence that might persuade people to visit the Cotswolds and explain why people might be persuaded.

Sentence:

_____

_____

Explanation:

_____

_____

_____

3

Marks

21. Read the section headed **But I don't like looking at the scenery**.

Use evidence from the text to explain why the writer gives the warning, *Don't dream too much though.*

_____

_____

2

22. Why is London *worth a week by itself?*

_____

1

23. Using evidence from the text, explain how the writer tries to make the *downsides* seem unimportant.

_____

_____

_____

_____

3

24. How does the writer try to persuade the reader to take holidays in England?

_____

1

Test A

Questions 25–36 are about *A London cab horse* on pages **12–13**.

25. What is the name of Black Beauty's new driver?

_____

_____

1

26. From the first paragraph, **find** and **copy** a phrase that shows that Captain must have been splendid in his youth.

_____

_____

1

27. Draw lines to join Polly and Dolly to their actions.

talked in gentle voices.

locked Black Beauty in his stall.

Polly and Dolly

cleaned Black Beauty.

petted Black Beauty.

1

Marks

28. Black Beauty found his first week *as a cab horse very* **trying**.

What does the word *trying* mean in this sentence?

_____

1

29. Black Beauty had not always been so well treated. **Find** and **copy** a phrase that shows this.

_____

1

30. Jerry put bars across the horses' stable to:

Tick **one**.

make the horses more comfortable. ☐

keep the horses in. ☐

make it easy to clean the horses. ☐

make it easy to feed the horses. ☐

1

31. Give **two** problems drinking too much water causes for a horse.

1. _____

2. _____

Marks

2

32. How do you know that this story is set in the past?

_____

1

33. The author uses Black Beauty to show:

Tick **one**.

animals work hard. ☐

horses are better than men. ☐

animal welfare is important. ☐

1

34. From the last paragraph, compare how Jerry and the other grooms look after their horses.

_____

_____

_____

2

35. How does the final paragraph link back to the beginning?

Marks

Tick **one**.

Feeding is mentioned in both paragraphs. ☐

Pulling the cab is mentioned in all paragraphs. ☐

Captain's story is mentioned in both paragraphs. ☐

Both paragraphs are about Sundays. ☐

1

36. At the end of the passage, Black Beauty says he learned of Captain's life story. Using evidence from the text, give **two** things that the story might include.

1. _____

2. _____

2

End of test

Test A Marks

Question	Focus	Possible marks	Actual marks
1	Information/key details	1	
2	Identifying/explaining how information is related	1	
3	Identifying/explaining choice of words and phrases	1	
4	Making inferences	1	
5	Meanings of words	2	
6	Making inferences	1	
7	Making inferences	1	
8	Information/key details	2	
9	Meanings of words	2	
10	Predicting	2	
11	Summarise	1	
12	Identifying/explaining how information is related	2	
13	Making inferences	1	
14	Information/key details	1	
15	Making inferences	1	
16	Information/key details	1	
17	Making inferences	1	
18	Making inferences	2	
19	Identifying/explaining choice of words and phrases	1	
20	Making inferences	3	
21	Making inferences	2	
22	Making inferences	1	
23	Making inferences	3	
24	Making inferences	1	
25	Information/key details	1	
26	Making inferences	1	
27	Information/key details	1	
28	Meanings of words	1	
29	Making inferences	1	
30	Information/key details	1	
31	Information/key details	2	
32	Making inferences	1	
33	Making inferences	1	
34	Making comparisons	2	
35	Making inferences	1	
36	Making inferences	2	
	Total	**50**	

■SCHOLASTIC National Curriculum SATs Tests

Test B

Into the Underworld

A river of rain ran down the leadlight window. Another dreary Sunday. James hated Sundays: the endless prayer meetings; the tedious hymns; the obligatory Amens; and, the dead, goldfish eyes of the congregation. Today would be different. Today he would escape! Already he had reached the first level of the steeple. He had never been allowed here before. This was forbidden territory.

The great bell tower loomed above James like a signpost to the heavens. Panting heavily, he paused for breath, leaned against the wall and looked around. What a let-down! A few pieces of broken plaster from the ceiling speckled the floor and there was some evidence that pigeons had once used the tower as a home but otherwise there seemed little of interest to reward the risks he had taken in going there. James let out a sigh of exasperation and turned for the stairs. He was about to go down when his eye caught something he hadn't seen at first. In the corner, half-hidden in shadow, was a chest.

What could be in it? James moved carefully across the room, anxious not to make too much noise on the squeaky floorboards. He knelt in front of the chest and examined it carefully. Two large leather straps crossed its domed top and were fastened in buckles at the front. The once shiny clasp on the front of the chest was encrusted with rust but as far as James could see there was no lock.

What could be in it? Perhaps it was a dead body! The chest was certainly big enough to hide one inside it easily. If it was a dead body it would be in the best possible place as it

was only a short walk to the cemetery outside. If the chest did contain a body it must be a very old one as it was obvious from the dust that it hadn't been opened in years.

What could be in it? There was only one way to find out. James's fingers fumbled as he wrestled with the leather straps. Whoever had put these on hadn't meant them to be undone easily. He stood up and pushed against the chest with one foot in order to give himself extra leverage. Slowly he could feel the first strap loosen and then suddenly give way, catapulting him across the room.

Opening the chest caused a storm of dust to rage across the room, catching in the light like unknown galaxies floating in illuminated space. James cautiously returned to the chest. It was empty. Almost. Lying on the bottom of it was what appeared to be a large black blanket but on closer inspection it became clear that it was some sort of cloak. Hurriedly, James pulled it on and looked at his reflection spotted in the raindrops on the window.

"Magic!"

Suddenly he realised his father would be missing him. Hastily, he replaced the cloak in the chest. There would be time on other days to wear it properly. Today was not the day for such indulgences. With some regret, James closed the lid of the trunk and turned towards the staircase. He needed to get down before his absence was noticed and he did not know when he would be able to return to the bell tower.

"James!"

He stood, transfixed. It was his father's voice, anxious at the bottom of the stairs.

"James! Where are you? Are you up there?"

He could hear his father's feet ascending the spiral wooden staircase. Another few seconds and he would be there. James looked around helplessly for a place to hide. He dare not be caught up there. His father was the vicar of the parish. Punishment, if not an eye for an eye, a tooth for a tooth, would at least require him to turn the other cheek. In panic his eyes swept the room.

"Oh my God!" It was ironic that he named the only person who could possibly save him at that moment.

"Get in the box!"

James swirled round wildly, looking for the owner of the voice. There was nobody there!

"Get in the box!" The voice became more insistent.

As if in a dream James followed the instructions.

"Hide under the cloak. Close the lid. Quickly!"

As the lid slammed shut, James wondered about the wisdom of ever venturing upstairs, never mind hiding in a chest that was acting like a ventriloquist's dummy. He could hear his father reach the landing. James tried to make himself as small and insignificant as

he felt. All he could do was lie there and await whatever his father would do to him.

James's father could not understand it. He was sure he had heard movement and voices. Who was up there and where had they gone? He eyed the chest suspiciously. Aha! The only hiding place! Triumphantly he threw the lid of the chest backwards and stared at its contents.

The chest was empty!

Graham Fletcher (2015)

Modern-day pirates -

You couldn't write the script

In the movies

Hollywood has always loved pirates. From the swashbuckling exploits of Errol Flynn to his modern day equivalent, Johnny Depp in Pirates of the Caribbean, they have been portrayed as attractive, daring characters. Inevitably handsome, they make piracy acceptable through their witty one-liners and their hearts of gold. They are shown as being sea-faring Robin Hoods and we should love them for it.

It would be nice if the movie version of pirates was correct. However, it isn't. Pirates were ruthless criminals who had no regard for their victims. Somehow, the fact that their crimes took place at sea, often in exotic locations, a long time ago, has made them glamorous.

Modern piracy

It would also be nice if pirates had stayed in the past or in the cinemas. Unfortunately, they haven't. Modern-day piracy exists and is as dangerous today as it was 300 years ago. Forget any romantic notions you may have. Today's pirates don't wear striped T-shirts, eye patches or have the obligatory wooden leg. They don't talk in Pirate, sea-mates, and they don't tell jokes.

In fact, they just aren't funny at all. They use speed boats and carry assault rifles and rocket-propelled grenades to commit their crimes. They attack ships of all sizes, from small yachts to huge oil tankers and cruise liners.

So who are today's pirates and where can they be found? You are unlikely to encounter them if you are sailing around the Isle of Wight or off the east coast of England. They operate in much poorer areas of the world, for instance the coasts of Somalia, China and Indonesia. Of these, Somalia is the most dangerous region. In 2010, out of a worldwide total of 53 attacked ships, 43 were hijacked there. The targets might be those on board, as much as the cargo.

The current trend is for pirates to kidnap crews and demand a ransom from their employers, families or governments. This is proving to be a most profitable trade with figures for the release of prisoners running into millions of pounds.

Somalia is not a rich country. Money is a big incentive for the pirates. Many used to be ordinary fishermen but had their fishing grounds stolen or polluted. The rewards of piracy are tempting. Successful pirates live well. They are able to afford big houses and flashy cars. They can buy increasingly sophisticated weapons, enabling them to expand their pirate industry.

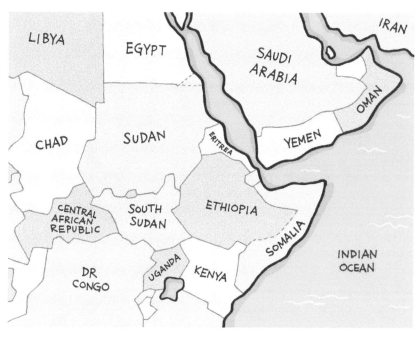

Some of them even have accountants to manage their finances! It is easy to see why, in a poor country, piracy is seen not so much as a crime but as a legitimate business activity.

Fighting piracy

There is some good news. Things are changing. Pirate attacks have decreased since 2008. However, it is reported that there are still over 40 ships and 400 hostages being held in Somalia alone. By 2012, international naval patrols had made it much more difficult for pirates to operate. This has pushed them into more open waters, further out from land, reducing the number of incidents but not ending them. For the first time, in 2012, Somali pirate attacks dropped by 80% compared with the previous year and for the first time more pirate attacks took place off the coast of West Africa than Somalia.

Maersk Alabama

Johnny Depp's escapades as Captain Jack Sparrow in the Caribbean will continue to ensure that pirates remain at least faintly romantic and attractive. However, Hollywood has come right up to date. The 2013 film *Captain Phillips* is based on the true story of the unarmed American cargo vessel *Maersk Alabama*, which was hijacked in 2009, 240 miles off the coast of Somalia, by four Somali pirates. The hero in this film is Captain Phillips and the film is told from his viewpoint. Multi-award winning Tom Hanks plays the ship's captain, Richard Phillips. Not surprisingly this event made headlines in America as it was the first time in over 200 years that such a thing had happened to an American ship. It is possible that we have taken the attitude that piracy happens in a faraway place to people we do not know and therefore is of little interest or relevance to us. Insurance companies foot the bills for ransoms so why worry about the cost? Perhaps *Captain Phillips* will start to show a more realistic view of life. However, if it does not make a lot of money, you can be sure that Hollywood will revert back to the buccaneers.

Snake

A snake came to my water-trough
On a hot, hot day, and I in pyjamas for the heat,
To drink there.

In the deep, strange-scented shade of the great dark carob-tree
I came down the steps with my pitcher
And must wait, must stand and wait, for there he was at the trough before
me.

He reached down from a fissure in the earth-wall in the gloom
And trailed his yellow-brown slackness soft-bellied down, over the edge
of the stone trough
And rested his throat upon the stone bottom,
And where the water had dripped from the tap, in a small clearness,
He sipped with his straight mouth,
Softly drank through his straight gums, into his slack long body,
Silently.

Someone was before me at my water-trough,
And I, like a second comer, waiting.

He lifted his head from his drinking, as cattle do,
And looked at me vaguely, as drinking cattle do,
And flickered his two-forked tongue from his lips, and mused a moment,
And stooped and drank a little more,
Being earth-brown, earth-golden from the burning bowels of the earth
On the day of Sicilian July, with Etna smoking.

The voice of my education said to me
He must be killed,
For in Sicily the black, black snakes are innocent, the gold are venomous.

And voices in me said, If you were a man
You would take a stick and break him now, and finish him off.

But must I confess how I liked him,
How glad I was he had come like a guest in quiet, to drink at my water-trough
And depart peaceful, pacified, and thankless,
Into the burning bowels of this earth?

Was it cowardice, that I dared not kill him?
Was it perversity, that I longed to talk to him?
Was it humility, to feel so honoured?
I felt so honoured.

From *Snake* by D H Lawrence

SCHOLASTIC National Curriculum SATs Tests

Marks

Questions 1–14 are about *Into the Underworld* on pages **28–29**.

1.

> *Another **dreary** Sunday.*

What does the word *dreary* mean in this sentence?

_____

1

2. Which of the following phrases suggest that James was disappointed by the bell tower?

Tick **two**.

This was forbidden territory ☐

What a let-down ☐

half-hidden in shadow ☐

was encrusted with rust ☐

there seemed little of interest ☐

1

3. Find and **copy** a phrase that shows that James had not been in the tower before.

_____

1

4. What is the effect of repeating *What could be in it?* at the start of three paragraphs?

_____

_____

Marks

1

5.

| James's fingers **fumbled** as he wrestled with the leather straps. |

What does the word *fumbled* mean in this sentence?

_____

1

6. Explain the effect on the reader of describing the dust as *catching in the light like unknown galaxies floating in illuminated space.*

_____

_____

2

7. Why do you think James gets into the chest?

_____

_____

Marks

1

8. What does James think the chest is acting like?

_____

1

9. Why does James's father open the chest *triumphantly*?

_____

_____

1

10. a. What do you think James's father was expecting to find in the chest?

_____

1

b. Find and **copy one** phrase/sentence to explain why James's father opened the chest.

_____

1

11. Write down **two** events in the story that are intended to make it exciting.

1. _____

2. _____

2

12. When he puts on the cloak, James says *Magic!* How does this link to the end of the passage?

_____

_____

1

13. a. What do you think James's father will do after finding that the chest is empty?

_____

1

b. Give a reason for your answer using evidence from the text.

_____

1

14. Put these events in the order they happen in the extract. Number I has been done for you.

James hears a voice coming from the chest.	
James climbs the bell tower.	I
James puts on the cloak.	
James opens the chest.	
James's father opens the chest.	
James's father calls to James.	

1

Marks

Questions 15–24 are about *Modern-day pirates* on pages **30–31**.

15. Hollywood's pirates are:

Tick **one**.

handsome. ☐

brutal. ☐

ugly. ☐

criminals. ☐

1

16. What does the phrase *Unfortunately, they haven't* tell us about the author's attitude to modern pirates?

_____

1

17. How are modern-day pirates different from their fictional portrayal?

Give **one** example.

_____

1

Marks

18. a. Where do most piracy incidents occur?

Tick **one**.

Around the Isle of Wight ☐

The coasts of Somalia ☐

Off the east coast of England ☐

The coasts of France ☐

1

b. Why do you think piracy occurs here?

_____

_____

1

19. Draw lines to match these sentences to the correct endings.

| Many pirates used to be | a business activity. |

| Successful pirates are | money of some pirates. |

| Accountants manage the | rich and live well. |

| In poor countries piracy is seen as | fishermen. |

1

20. Give **three** ways that piracy has changed in recent years.

1. _____

2. _____

3. _____

Marks

3

21. Why have pirate attacks decreased in recent years?

_____

_____

1

22. How does Hollywood's portrayal of events on the *Maersk Alabama* in the film *Captain Phillips* differ from the way it portrayed pirates in earlier films?

Give **three** examples.

1. _____

2. _____

3. _____

3

Reading

Test B

23. Put a tick in the correct box to show whether each of the following statements is a **fact** or **opinion**.

	Fact	Opinion
It is easy to see why, in a poor country, piracy is seen not so much as a crime but as a legitimate business activity.		
For the first time, in 2012, Somali pirate attacks dropped.		
Captain Phillips is based on the true story of the unarmed American cargo vessel Maersk Alabama.		
However, if it does not make a lot of money, you can be sure that Hollywood will revert back to the buccaneers.		

24. Why do you think Hollywood produces films about pirates?

_____

_____

Marks

1

2

■SCHOLASTIC National Curriculum SATs Tests

Marks

Questions 25–35 are about *Snake* on page **32**.

25.

A snake came to my water-trough

What does the word *water-trough* mean in this sentence?

_____

_____   1

26. Why does the writer *stand and wait* for the snake to finish drinking?

_____

_____   1

27. What colour was the snake?

_____

_____   1

28. In the verse beginning *He reached down from a fissure*, what impressions does the writer want us to have of the snake? Give **two** reasons.

_____

_____   2

Marks

29. Explain why the writer thought he should have killed the snake.

_____

_____

1

30. Read the verses beginning *The voice of my education* and *And voices.*

Summarise what the voices say to the poet.

_____

_____

1

31. a. Find and **copy** a phrase that the voices in him use to try to persuade the writer to kill the snake.

_____

1

b. Explain why the writer might be persuaded by the phrase.

_____

1

32. Explain why the writer doesn't kill the snake.

Marks

_____

_____

2

33. Number the events below to show the order in which they happen in the poem. Number 1 has been done for you.

The snake leaves.	
The writer sees the snake.	1
The snake looks at the writer.	
The snake drinks.	
The writer feels honoured.	

1

34. Find and **copy three** phrases that show that the writer was impressed by the snake.

1. _____

2. _____

3. _____

Marks

3

35. What is the effect on the reader of the questions in the last verse?

_____

1

End of test

Question	Focus	Possible marks	Actual marks
1	Meanings of words	1	
2	Making inferences	1	
3	Making inferences	1	
4	Identifying/explaining choice of words and phrases	1	
5	Meanings of words	1	
6	Identifying/explaining choice of words and phrases	2	
7	Making inferences	1	
8	Information/key details	1	
9	Meanings of words	1	
10	Making inferences	2	
11	Making inferences	2	
12	Identifying/explaining how information is related	1	
13	Predicting	2	
14	Summarise	1	
15	Information/key details	1	
16	Meanings of words	1	
17	Information/key details	1	
18	Information/key details / Making inferences	2	
19	Information/key details	1	
20	Information/key details	3	
21	Making inferences	1	
22	Making comparisons	3	
23	Making inferences	1	
24	Making inferences	2	
25	Meanings of words	1	
26	Making inferences	1	
27	Information/key details	1	
28	Making inferences	2	
29	Making inferences	1	
30	Summarise	1	
31	Making inferences	2	
32	Making inferences	2	
33	Summarise	1	
34	Information/key details	3	
35	Making inferences	1	
	Total	**50**	

Test C

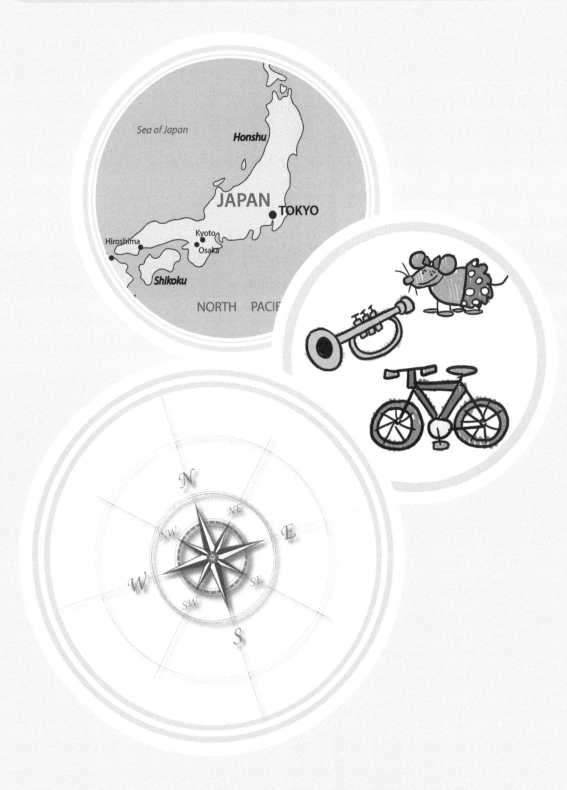

The best Christmas ever

23 December

This is going to be the BEST Christmas ever! I am going to get a new bike. I am sure of it. I have been dropping hints since July that it was time that I had some transport of my own.

24 December CHRISTMAS EVE

For the first time ever, I have been allowed to stay up for the late evening carol service. The vicar said I was a very good little girl. I almost bit his hand off! Minnie, my six-year-old sister, has not been allowed to go. My dad, for reasons beyond my understanding, always calls her Mouse.

To make matters worse, he has recently started calling Mum 'Minnie'. I am totally confused.

Gran and Grandad have come to stay. They couldn't come any earlier as they have both been working. I cannot understand why the pair of them didn't retire years ago. They must both be well over ninety.

I am sharing Minnie's bedroom as my grandparents are using mine. That's fine. They can stay as long as they want.

25 December CHRISTMAS DAY

6.00 This is the worst Christmas ever! I can't wait for my grandparents to go home. Minnie woke up every hour during the night and said, "Has he been?" She has now gone downstairs, where, judging from the noise she is making, he clearly has been. I am trying to disappear into the bed so she won't see me when she comes back.

7.00 Minnie is back. I am pretending to be asleep. This is not easy when you are being bashed with a toy trumpet.

8.00 I have given in and got up. Actually, I would have liked to have got up and seen my bike at 6 o'clock but that's what little kids do. When you are as grown up and mature as I am, you have to take things slowly.

9.00 This really is the worst Christmas ever. It wasn't there. They haven't bought it. No bike! Instead they have bought me a pair of roller skates. They aren't even inline ones! My dad said he knew I'd wanted some transport of my own so he'd got me four-wheel drive for my feet. I hate them all.

I am now back in Minnie's bedroom. This writing is getting smudged by my tears as I write it, using a rather cool fountain pen my gran bought. She said it was so I'd stop using all that text rubbish. GR8! IMHO she should mind her own business. BTW, I don't use text speak. LOL!

25 December CHRISTMAS DAY

10.00 This is the BEST CHRISTMAS EVER!!!!! Dad called me downstairs and told me to go in the garage. My bike was there! He had been messing all the time. I would have kissed him but that's not the kind of thing mature 13-year-olds like me do.

3.00 The queen has visited us again via the modern miracle of television. I don't know why she bothers. Everyone was asleep – as usual – except Minnie, who was playing Jingle Bells on her toy trumpet.

4.00 The toy trumpet is in the bin and Minnie is howling. Genuine heart-warming Christmas tune or not, 57 times without a break was too much. 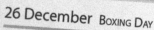 Everyone is awake now. Dad has retrieved the trumpet from the bin and I am in disgrace. Grounded till tomorrow.

5.00 The toy trumpet is back in the bin. Dad has put it there. Apparently, genuine heart-warming Christmas tune or not, 24 times without a break was too much. The man has no patience. Minnie is howling again but I am not grounded any more – she is! This really is the best Christmas ever.

26 December BOXING DAY

I've crashed it, smashed it, dashed it. The bike goes like a rocket. Chris Hoy and Bradley Wiggins on a tandem, Olympic champions or not, couldn't have kept up. Unfortunately, the brakes are useless. I went straight through our fence. I'm OK but we need a new fence. The front wheel on my bike is so bent that it resembles a harp. Perhaps I could learn to play Jingle Bells on it. I can't get it mended for a week because the shops are closed. This really has been the WORST Christmas ever.

Overview

Japan lies in the Pacific Ocean to the east of Russia, North Korea and South Korea. It has over 6000 islands but the four largest ones make up over 90% of the country's area.

Almost 75% of the country is mountainous and forested. This leaves very little room for the population of over 120 million, making Japan one of the most densely populated countries in the world. The capital, Tokyo, and its surrounding districts have over 30 million people living in them. This is over twice as many as London.

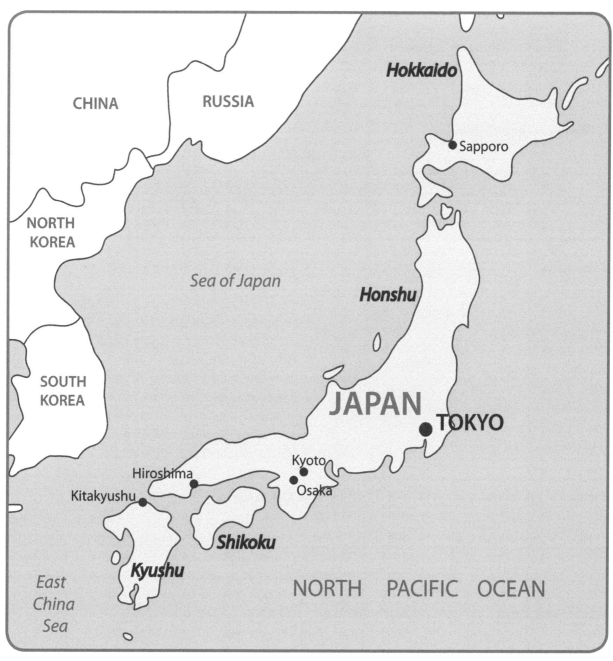

Weather

Unlike Britain, most of Japan has two main seasons:

1 A hot, damp summer.

2 A cooler, drier winter.

However, this varies from north to south. In the north around Hokkaido, the winters are long and cold. On Honshu's west coast, there is heavy snow in the winter. The Central Highlands have large temperature differences between summer and winter, and between day and night. There is not much rain but winters usually have a lot of snowfall. The Pacific coast has milder winters with little snow and hot, damp summers because of the predominantly south-easterly winds.

Average temperatures for Tokyo

Degrees Centigrade												
High	10	11	14	20	24	27	32	31	28	22	17	12
Low	-1	0	3	8	12	18	22	23	19	13	16	1
	Jan	Feb	Mar	Apr	May	Jun	July	Aug	Sept	Oct	Nov	Dec

Average rainfall for Tokyo

Millimetres of rainfall											
40	20	70	90	110	140	160	230	210	170	50	30
Jan	Feb	Mar	Apr	May	Jun	July	Aug	Sept	Oct	Nov	Dec

Economy

Japan is a major world economy. In 2012, Japan was ranked third in the world. It relies heavily on manufacturing. It has massive electronic companies like Sony, Hitachi and Toshiba. The car giants Mazda, Toyota and Nissan all have their homes there as well as the motorcycle manufacturers Honda, Suzuki and Kawasaki. The main trading partners for the country are China and the USA.

Sport

Japan is not recognised as a world leader in any of the major team sports such as football. Traditionally, sumo wrestling is regarded as the national sport. This attracts large crowds and the most successful wrestlers are celebrities with household names. Other martial arts such as judo, karate and kendo are also popular. Although Japan is not prominent in the world of sport, its achievements in this area are growing. In the past, its men's football team has reached the final stages of the FIFA World Cup and it co-hosted the competition with South Korea in 2002. Its rugby union team is the most successful in Asia, winning the Asian Five Nations competition six times. In 2019 the Rugby World Cup will be held in Japan. Sapporo and Nagano have both hosted the Winter Olympics and in 2020 the Summer Olympics will take place in Tokyo, making it the first Asian city to host the games twice. Despite all of this, baseball remains the country's number one spectator sport.

The future

Japan is developing as a tourist destination. Its food is becoming known around the world. Its education system ranks sixth in the world and despite the effects of the 2009 global recession followed by an earthquake and tsunami in March 2011, Japan is still financially secure. Japan's flag is the Rising Sun and, like that, its future seems bright.

Reaching Treasure Island

Adapted from *Treasure Island* by Robert Louis Stevenson

Treasure Island is one of the most famous pirate stories ever written. It tells the story of young Jim Hawkins, who accidentally joins a gang of pirates led by Long John Silver, a one-legged villain who will stop at nothing to get what he wants. The treasure that the pirates are looking for is buried on Treasure Island. In this extract, Jim describes the scene after they arrive at the island.

The appearance of the island when I came on deck next morning was altogether changed. Although the breeze had now utterly ceased, we had made a great deal of way during the night and were now lying calmly about half a mile to the south-east of the low eastern coast. Grey-coloured woods covered a large part of the surface. This even tint was broken up by streaks of yellow sand in the lower lands and by many tall trees of the pine family, out-topping the others – some singly, some in clumps; but the general colouring was uniform and sad. The hills ran up clear above the vegetation in spires of naked rock. All were strangely shaped, and the Spy-glass, which was by three or four hundred feet the tallest hill on the island, was likewise the strangest in appearance, running up sheer from almost every side and then suddenly cut off at the top like a pedestal to put a statue on.

The *Hispaniola* was rolling in the ocean swell. The rudder was banging to and fro, and the whole ship creaking, groaning, and jumping like an injured animal. I had to cling tight to the rope, and the world turned giddily before my eyes, for though I was a good enough sailor normally, this standing still and being rolled about like a bottle was a thing I never learned to stand without a qualm or so, above all in the morning, on an empty stomach.

Perhaps it was this – perhaps it was the look of the island, with its grey, melancholy woods, and wild stone spires, and the surf that we could both see and hear foaming and thundering on the steep beach – although the sun shone bright and hot, and the shore birds were fishing and crying all around us, and you would have thought anyone would have been glad to get to land after being so long at sea. My heart sank, as the saying is, into my boots; and from the first look onward, I hated the very thought of Treasure Island.

We had a dreary morning's work before us, for there was no sign of any wind, and the boats had to be got out and manned, and the ship sailed three or four miles round the corner of the island and up the narrow passage to the haven behind Skeleton Island. I volunteered for one of the boats, where I had, of course, no business. The heat was sweltering, and the men grumbled fiercely over their work. Anderson was in command of my boat, and instead of keeping the crew in order, he grumbled as loud as the worst.

"Well," he said with an oath, "it's not forever."

I thought this was a very bad sign, for up to that day the men had gone briskly and willingly about their business; but the very sight of the island seemed to have made them give up working.

All the way in, Long John stood by the steersman and conned the ship. He knew the passage like the palm of his hand, and he never hesitated once.

"There's a strong current," he said, "and this here passage has been dug out, in a manner of speaking, with a spade."

We stopped just where the anchor was in the chart, about a third of a mile from each shore, the mainland on one side and Skeleton Island on the other. The bottom was clean sand. The plunge of our anchor sent up clouds of birds wheeling and crying over the woods, but in less than a minute they were down again and all was once more silent.

The place was entirely land-locked, buried in woods, the trees coming right down to high-water mark, the shores mostly flat, and the hilltops standing round at a distance in a sort of amphitheatre, one here, one there. Two little rivers, or rather two swamps, emptied out into this pond, as you might call it; and the foliage round that part of the shore had a kind of poisonous brightness. From the ship we could see nothing of the house or its walls, for they were quite buried among trees; and if it had not been for the existence of the chart, we might have believed that we were the first that had ever anchored there since the island arose out of the seas.

There was not a breath of air moving, nor a sound but that of the surf booming half a mile away along the beaches and against the rocks outside. A peculiar stagnant smell hung over the anchorage – a smell of sodden leaves and rotting tree trunks. I observed the doctor sniffing and sniffing, like someone tasting a bad egg.

"I don't know about treasure," he said, "but I'll stake my life there's fever here."

If the behaviour of the men had been alarming in the boat, it became truly threatening when they had come back on board the *Hispaniola*. They lay about the deck growling together in talk. The slightest order was received with a black look and grudgingly and carelessly obeyed. Even the honest hands must have caught the infection, for there was not one man aboard to mend another. Mutiny, it was plain, hung over us like a thunder cloud.

Glossary:

Melancholy – sad

Steersman – the person who steers the ship

Amphitheatre – an open, circular building with a stage in the centre

Foliage – plant leaves

Mutiny – when sailors take over the ship from the captain

Marks

Questions 1–13 are about *The best Christmas ever* on pages **47–48**.

1. On 23 December, why did the writer think this would be the best Christmas ever?

Tick **one**.

She would be allowed to go to the late night carol service. ☐

She would get a bike. ☐

Her grandparents were coming to stay. ☐

She would be more mature. ☐

1

2. Circle **one**. Minnie is the writer's:

sister.   mother.

gran.   pet mouse.

1

3. Explain why the writer's father calls her sister *Mouse*.

_____

1

4. Give **two** reasons why the writer was disappointed with the roller skates.

Marks

1. _____

2. _____

2

5. Who bought the fountain pen for the writer?

_____

1

6. Find **two** things that the writer does not do now that she is a mature, grown-up thirteen-year-old.

1. _____

2. _____

2

7. Give **two** reasons why the bent bike wheel might resemble a harp.

1. _____

2. _____

2

Marks

8. How does the writer try to create humour through the use of the trumpet?

_____

_____

_____

3

9. Explain why the writer's father put the trumpet in the bin.

_____

1

10. How many days are covered by the diary?

_____

1

11. What would be a good alternative title for this extract?

Tick **one**.

My new bike ☐

The worst Christmas ever ☐

Minnie and the trumpet ☐

Jingle bells ☐

1

12. Look at the entry for 25 December, Christmas Day.

a. How is the structure of this entry different to the other entries?

_____

b. What effect does the structure of the Christmas Day entry have on the reader?

_____

13. Explain how and why the writer's attitude to Christmas keeps changing.

_____

_____

_____

_____

_____

Marks

1

1

3

Marks

Questions 14–24 are about *Japan* on pages **49–50**.

14. What are the names of the four main islands of Japan?

1. _____

2. _____

3. _____

4. _____

1

15. Japan has:

Tick **two**.

a wet, hot winter. ☐

a hot, damp summer. ☐

a cooler, drier winter. ☐

a cooler, drier summer. ☐

1

16.

| predominantly south-easterly winds |

In this sentence *predominantly* is nearest in meaning to:

Tick **one**.

rare. ☐

unusual. ☐

mostly. ☐

continuous. ☐

1

17. Look at the average temperature and rainfall tables.

   a. Which month has the highest amount of rainfall?

   _____

1

   b. Which month has the lowest average temperature?

   _____

1

18. Compare the winters in the north and on the Pacific coast.

_____

_____

2

Marks

19. Name **three** things Japan manufactures.

1. _____

2. _____

3. _____

1

20. Compare the achievements of Japan's national rugby union and football teams.

_____

_____

2

21. Look at the final sentence. **Find** and **copy one fact** and **one opinion**.

Fact: _____

Opinion: _____

2

22. Match the events below to the year in which they happened.

There was a global recession.	2002
Japan co-hosted the FIFA World Cup.	2009
Japan was ranked third in the world's economies.	2011
There was an earthquake and a tsunami.	2012

1

23. Where are you most likely to find this article?

Tick **one**.

In a geography textbook ☐

In a newspaper ☐

In a holiday brochure ☐

In a teenage magazine ☐

Marks

1

24. Which of the following titles is the most appropriate alternative to *Japan*?

Tick **one**.

Holidaying in Japan ☐

Japanese culture ☐

A snapshot of Japan ☐

Asian weather ☐

1

Marks

> **Questions** 25–37 are about *Reaching Treasure Island* on pages **51–52**.

25. At what time of day does Jim say the appearance of the island was different?

_____

1

26. What colour is most of the island?

_____

1

27. The *Hispaniola* is:

Tick **one**.

a bird. ☐

a sailor. ☐

a rock. ☐

a ship. ☐

1

Marks

28. How does the author show the condition of the sea in the second paragraph?

Give **one** example and explain its effect.

_____

_____

2

29.

| rolled about like a bottle |

What does _like a bottle_ mean in this phrase?

_____

1

30.

| My heart sank... into my boots |

What does this tell us about the author's feelings when he sees the island?

_____

_____

1

31. The men on the boat seem very unhappy.

Find and **copy one** phrase or sentence that supports this view.

_____

1

32.

> *There was not a breath of air moving, nor a sound* **but** *that of the surf booming half a mile away along the beaches and against the rocks outside.*

Marks

What does the word *but* mean in this sentence?

_____

1

33. The doctor's words, *"...there's fever here"*, spoken just before the last paragraph, tell us:

Tick **one**.

they are all ill. ☐

they will all die. ☐

the island is an unhealthy place to go. ☐

someone has a temperature. ☐

1

34. Read the final paragraph. What do you think is likely to happen next?

_____

1

35.

> ***Mutiny***, *it was plain, hung over us like a thunder cloud.*

In this sentence, *mutiny* is nearest in meaning to:

Tick **one**.

happiness. ☐

anger. ☐

rebellion. ☐

agreement. ☐

Marks

1

36. Why had Long John Silver taken them all to the island?

_____

1

37. The story is told in the first person. Give **one** reason why the author has done this.

_____

1

End of test

Question	Focus	Possible marks	Actual marks
1	Information/key details	1	
2	Information/key details	1	
3	Making inferences	1	
4	Making inferences	2	
5	Information/key details	1	
6	Information/key details	2	
7	Making inferences	2	
8	Identifying/explaining choice of words and phrases	3	
9	Making inferences	1	
10	Information/key details	1	
11	Summarise	1	
12	Identifying/explaining how information is related	2	
13	Making inferences	3	
14	Information/key details	1	
15	Information/key details	1	
16	Meanings of words	1	
17	Information/key details	2	
18	Making comparisons	2	
19	Information/key details	1	
20	Making comparisons	2	
21	Making inferences	2	
22	Information/key details	1	
23	Making inferences	1	
24	Summarise	1	
25	Information/key details	1	
26	Information/key details	1	
27	Information/key details	1	
28	Making inferences	2	
29	Meanings of words	1	
30	Making inferences	1	
31	Information/key details	1	
32	Meanings of words	1	
33	Meanings of words	1	
34	Predicting	1	
35	Meanings of words	1	
36	Making inferences	1	
37	Identifying/explaining how information is related	1	
	Total	**50**	

Marking and assessing the papers

The mark schemes provide detailed examples of correct answers (although other variations/ phrasings are often acceptable) and an explanation about what the answer should contain to be awarded a mark or marks.

Although the mark scheme sometimes contains alternative suggestions for correct answers, some children may find other ways of expressing a correct answer. When marking these tests, exercise judgement when assessing the accuracy or relevance of an answer and give credit for correct responses.

Marks table

At the end of each test there is a table for you to insert the number of marks achieved for each question. This will enable you to see which areas your child needs to practise further.

National standard in Reading

The mark that your child gets in the test paper will be known as the 'raw score' (for example, '22' in 22/50). The raw score will be converted to a scaled score and children achieving a scaled score of 100 or more will achieve the national standard in that subject. These 'scaled scores' enable results to be reported consistently year-on-year.

The guidance in the table below shows the marks that children need to achieve to reach the national standard. This should be treated as a guide only, as the number of marks may vary. You can also find up-to-date information about scaled scores on our website: www.scholastic.co.uk/nationaltests

Marks achieved	Standard
0–27	Has not met the national standard in Reading for KS2
28–50	Has met the national standard in Reading for KS2

Mark scheme for Test A (pages 7–26)

Q	Answers	Marks
1	**Award 1 mark** for: little wolves.	1
2	**Award 1 mark** for answers such as: • It makes the reader feel like the passage is speaking directly to them • It makes the reader see the passage from the wolves' point of view	1
3	**Award 1 mark** for answers such as: • It makes it seem as if the wolf did nothing to the pigs. • The wolf doesn't deserve what happened to it.	1
4	**Award 1 mark** for: The most wanted criminals.	1
5	**Award 2 marks** for: • The wolves should avoid the pigs. • The wolves should make sure there is a large distance between them and the pigs. **Award 1 mark** for one of the above.	2
6	**Award 1 mark** for: A survival manual has been written.	1
7	**Award 1 mark** for answers that show understanding of the idea that the pigs look innocent and/or childlike but in reality are dangerous.	1
8	**Award 2 marks** for: • avoid contact • run away at once **Award 1 mark** for answers that include one of the above.	2
9	**Award 2 marks** for: • straw • sticks **Award 1 mark** for answers that include one of the above.	2
10	**Award 2 marks** for answers that suggest the pigs will come down the chimney and be boiled in the pan of water on the fire. **Award 1 mark** for answers that include one of the above.	2
11	**Award 1 mark** for: frightened at the beginning; happy at the end	1
12	**Award 2 marks** for full answers that include: • It gives advice on how to deal with pigs. • It makes it seem as if the pigs can be beaten. **Award 1 mark** for answers that include one of the above.	2
13	**Award 1 mark** for: • dangerous. • untrustworthy.	1
14	**Award 1 mark** for over fifty years.	1

Q	Answers	Marks
15	**Award 1 mark** for perhaps.	1
16	**Award 1 mark** for 75 miles.	1
17	**Award 1 mark** for all correct:	1

	Fact	Opinion
Blackpool and Southport are both in the north-west.	✓	
Blackpool is big and brash.		✓
Southport is more sedate.		✓
Blackpool and Southport both have wide expanses of golden sand.	✓	

Q	Answers	Marks
18	**Award 2 marks** for: • It is packed with mountains and magnificent views. • It has picture-postcard Christmas scenes. **Award 1 mark** for either of the above.	2
19	**Award 1 mark** for alliteration.	1
20	**Award 3 marks** for answers that include any of the following and a detailed explanation: • Nestling among them are chocolate-box villages that seem to have come straight out of history. • They are exactly what people think of when they picture English villages. • Some of them have romantic, almost ancient names like Bourton-on-the-Water, conjuring up images of days gone by. • Who could resist the mysteries suggested by the Slaughters, twin villages with a gruesome name? Detailed explanations could include, for example: • People might want to go to see the chocolate-box villages because they sound very attractive. • People who are interested in history might want to go to see the old villages. **Award 2 marks** for answers that include any of the above and some explanation. Explanations could include: • People might want to go to see the chocolate-box villages. • People who are interested in history might want to go. **Award 1 mark** for answers that include one sentence but do not give any explanation.	3
21	**Award 2 marks** for answers that include 'the bends are very tricky' and an explanation that refers to the quote. For example: If the readers are dreaming, they might crash because the bends are very tricky. **Award 1 mark** for answers that include 'the bends are very tricky' but do not give an explanation or answers that give an explanation but do not refer closely to the text.	2

SCHOLASTIC National Curriculum SATs Tests

22   **Award 1 mark** for answers that indicate that there is a lot to do there. | 1

23   **Award 3 marks** for answers that give a full explanation using evidence from all three downsides. | 3

For example: The writer tries to make the downsides seem unimportant by making them seem minor. The writer says it never rains long. The traffic can be heavy but the wait will be worth it. There is so much to do that you won't be able to choose.

Award 2 marks for answers that explain but only use two examples.
Award 1 mark for answers that give some explanation and an example.

24   **Award 1 mark** for answers that explain how the text would persuade. Answers must be text-specific. For example: The text tells the reader that you do not have to go abroad for good beaches **or** It gives the reader lots of choices of scenery or activity **or** It shows that there are no real drawbacks to holidays in England. | 1

Do not accept answers such as 'It sounds like a nice place' or 'It sounds interesting'.

25   **Award 1 mark** for Jerry. Accept Jeremiah. | 1

26   **Award 1 mark** for any of the following: | 1
- He still had a proud way of holding his head and arching his neck.
- He was a high-bred, fine-mannered, noble old horse, every inch of him.
- He belonged to an officer in the cavalry and used to lead the regiment.

27   **Award 1 mark** for both correct: | 1

Polly and Dolly → talked in gentle voices.
Polly and Dolly → petted Black Beauty.

28   **Award 1 mark** for 'difficult' or similar. | 1
Do accept 'tiring'.

29   **Award 1 mark** for any of the following: | 1
- It was a great treat to be petted again and talked to in a gentle voice
- The broken knees
- The 'Black Beauty' of olden times

30   **Award 1 mark** for make the horses more comfortable. | 1

31   **Award 2 marks** for both of: | 2
- It chills a horse's stomach.
- It spoils a horse's breathing.

Award 1 mark for one of the above.

Q	Answers	Marks
32	**Award 1 mark** for any one of: • Captain was in the Crimean War. • Cabs are not pulled by horses nowadays. • There are carts and carriages on the streets in the story but we have cars and lorries.	1
33	**Award 1 mark** for animal welfare is important.	1
34	**Award 2 marks** for: • Jerry gave lots of clean water which he allowed to stand by them both day and night. **and** • Other grooms often went home to their beer, leaving the horses without water for hours. **Award 1 mark** for an answer that includes some of the above but does not compare.	2
35	**Award 1 mark** for Captain's story is mentioned in both paragraphs	1
36	**Award 2 marks** for any two of: • Captain went to the Crimean War. • He belonged to an officer in the cavalry. • He used to lead the regiment. **Award 1 mark** for any one of the above.	2

Mark scheme for Test B (pages 27–45)

Q	Answers	Marks
1	**Award 1 mark** for answers that suggest boring, tedious, slow or similar.	1
2	**Award 1 mark** for: • What a let-down • there seemed little of interest	1
3	**Award 1 mark** for 'He had never been allowed' or 'This was forbidden territory'.	1
4	**Award 1 mark** for answers that recognise why the feature is used. Possible responses: • It makes you wonder what could happen and want to know the answer. • It builds tension. • It makes the reader feel how much James wants to know what is in the chest.	1
5	**Award 1 mark** for 'struggled', 'groped' or similar. The answer must show some understanding of James not finding it easy to open the chest.	1
6	**Award 2 marks** for answers that show a full understanding of the simile. Possible response: • The dust is likened to small planets floating in space. This helps the reader understand what the dust looked like because the pieces of dust seem very small in the space of the room. **Award 1 mark** for answers that show a general understanding of the use of figurative language. Possible responses: • It paints a picture that the reader can see. • It helps the reader to understand what the dust looked like.	2
7	**Award 1 mark** for a reasonable inference. Possible responses: • It is the only place to hide. • He is trying to hide from his father. • The voice tells him to do it. • He panics.	1
8	**Award 1 mark** for a ventriloquist's dummy.	1
9	**Award 1 mark** for answers that indicate that James's father thinks he has caught whoever/whatever is in the tower.	1
10	**a. Award 1 mark** for answers that include James, an intruder or similar.	1
	b. Award 1 mark for answers that include 'He was sure he had heard movement and voices' or 'The only hiding place!'	1

Q	Answers	Marks
11	**Award 2 marks** for answers that identify two events. Possible responses: • James opening the chest. • James being surprised by his father's voice at the bottom of the stairs. • James's father coming up the stairs. • When James first hears the voice in the chest. • James's father seeing the chest. • The chest being empty when James's father opens it. **Award 1 mark** for answers that only include one event.	2
12	**Award 1 mark** for answers that show the link between magic and James disappearing.	1
13	**a. Award 1 mark** for any likely answer. Possible responses: • He will continue looking for James. • He will give up looking for James. **b. Award 1 mark** for a reason that is supported by the text. Possible responses: • He is worried about where James might be and wants to find him because he sounded 'anxious'. • He thinks that he must have been mistaken about hearing something in the bell tower.	1 1
14	**Award 1 mark** for all correct: <table><tr><td>James hears a voice coming from the chest.</td><td>5</td></tr><tr><td>James climbs the bell tower.</td><td>1</td></tr><tr><td>James puts on the cloak.</td><td>3</td></tr><tr><td>James opens the chest.</td><td>2</td></tr><tr><td>James's father opens the chest.</td><td>6</td></tr><tr><td>James's father calls to James.</td><td>4</td></tr></table>	1
15	**Award 1 mark** for handsome.	1
16	**Award 1 mark** for answers that show understanding of the writer's opposition to pirates. Possible responses: • It tells us the writer wishes pirates did not exist now. • The writer thinks pirates are a bad thing.	1

■SCHOLASTIC National Curriculum SATs Tests

Q	Answers	Marks

17 **Award 1 mark** for answers that include one of the following.
Possible responses:
- They are ruthless.
- They are not romantic.
- They are not funny – don't tell jokes, don't talk Pirate.
- They don't wear pirate outfits – striped T-shirts, eye patches, wooden legs.
- They use speed boats, rifles and rocket-propelled grenades.
- They attack all kinds of ships.

Marks: 1

18 **a. Award 1 mark** for: The coasts of Somalia.

Marks: 1

b. Award 1 mark for answers that give reasons.
Possible responses:
- Somalia is a poor country.
- The pirates used to be fishermen but cannot catch fish any longer.

Marks: 1

19 **Award 1 mark** for all correct:

Many pirates used to be	→	a business activity.
Successful pirates are	→	money of some pirates.
Accountants manage the	→	rich and live well.
In poor countries piracy is seen as	→	fishermen.

Marks: 1

20 **Award 3 marks** for answers that include three of the following:
- Pirates are taking hostages and demanding ransoms rather than just taking cargoes.
- Pirates are being forced into more open water, away from the coast.
- Piracy is reducing.
- There is more piracy off the west coast of Africa now than off Somalia.

Award 2 marks for answers that include two of the above.
Award 1 mark for answers that include one of the above.

Marks: 3

21 **Award 1 mark** for answers that explain that international patrols have made it more difficult for pirates to operate.

Marks: 1

22 **Award 3 marks** for answers that include any three of:
- *Captain Phillips* shows a more realistic view of piracy.
- The events are seen from the victim's (Captain Phillips's) point of view, which is different from before.
- Hollywood has made the captain the hero, not the pirates.
- Earlier films were romantic/glamorised and showed events from the pirates' point of view.
- Previously, Hollywood made the pirates look handsome, good-hearted and heroic. This film shows the horror of an attack.

Award 2 marks for answers that include two of the above responses.
Award 1 mark for answers that include one of the above responses.

Marks: 3

Q	Answers	Marks
23	**Award 1 mark** for all correct:	1

	Fact	Opinion
It is easy to see why, in a poor country, piracy is seen not so much as a crime but as a legitimate business activity.		✓
For the first time, in 2012, Somali pirate attacks dropped.	✓	
Captain Phillips is based on the true story of the unarmed American cargo vessel *Maersk Alabama*.	✓	
However, if it does not make a lot of money, you can be sure that Hollywood will revert back to the buccaneers.		✓

Q	Answers	Marks
24	**Award 2 marks** for answers that include: • Pirates are popular in cinemas. • Pirate films make lots of money. **Award 1 mark** for answers that include one of the above.	2
25	**Award 1 mark** for a container of water or similar.	1
26	**Award 1 mark** for answers that show that he was afraid of the snake and did not want to disturb it.	1
27	**Award 1 mark** for yellow-brown. Accept gold.	1
28	**Award 2 marks** for answers that include two of the following: • It moved slowly. • It was soft-skinned. • It was thirsty. • It was beautiful. • It was brightly-coloured. **Award 1 mark** for answers that include one of the above.	2
29	**Award 1 mark** for answers that show that the snake was venomous/poisonous/dangerous.	1
30	**Award 1 mark** for answers that include killing the snake with a stick or beating it to death or similar. **Do not award marks** for answers that just copy the text.	1
31	**a. Award 1 mark** for 'If you were a man'. **b. Award 1 mark** for answers that suggest the writer would be weak if he didn't do it.	1 1
32	**Award 2 marks** for any two of: • The writer liked the snake. • He was glad he had seen it. • He felt honoured to have seen it. **Award 1 mark** for one of the above.	2

Q	Answers		Marks
33	**Award 1 mark** for all correct:		1

The snake leaves.	4
The writer sees the snake.	1
The snake looks at the writer.	3
The snake drinks.	2
The writer feels honoured.	5

Q	Answers	Marks
34	**Award 3 marks** for answers that include all of the following: • I must confess how I liked him • How glad I was he had come • I felt so honoured **Award 2 marks** for answers that include two of the above. **Award 1 mark** for answers that include one of the above.	3
35	**Award 1 mark** for answers that indicate that the reader tries to answer the questions.	1

Mark scheme for Test C (pages 46–65)

Q	Answers	Marks
1	**Award 1 mark** for: She would get a bike.	1
2	**Award 1 mark** for: sister.	1
3	**Award 1 mark** for answers that show the connection between Minnie and Mouse – Minnie Mouse.	1
4	**Award 2 marks** for answers that include: ● She was expecting a bike. ● The skates weren't even inline ones. **Award 1 mark** for answers that include one of the above.	2
5	**Award 1 mark** for her gran or Gran.	1
6	**Award 2 marks** for answers that include: ● Get up early on Christmas Day. ● Kiss her father. **Award 1 mark** for answers that include one of the above.	2
7	**Award 2 marks** for: ● The spokes look like the strings of a harp. ● The bent wheel could look like the shape of a harp. **Award 1 mark** for answers that include one of the above.	2
8	**Award 3 marks** for full answers that include at least three of: ● Every time the trumpet appears, it causes trouble. ● The trumpet is used to annoy the writer. ● The writer gets into trouble for putting the trumpet in the bin. ● The trumpet is retrieved from the bin only for the writer's father to put it back again. **Award 2 marks** for answers that include at least two of the above. **Award 1 mark** for answers that include at least one of the above.	3
9	**Award 1 mark** for Minnie had played Jingle Bells 24 times without a break and this was too much for her father.	1
10	**Award 1 mark** for four.	1
11	**Award 1 mark** for The worst Christmas ever.	1
12	**a. Award 1 mark** for answers that explain it has times, or it goes through the events of the day in order.	1
	b. Award 1 mark for answers that explain it makes it easy to follow the events of the day, or it makes it easy to understand the writer's changing attitude.	1

SCHOLASTIC National Curriculum SATs Tests

Q	Answers	Marks

13   **Award 3 marks** for full answers that include reasons for the changing attitudes.   3

Possible response:
- Before Christmas Day, the writer thinks this will be the best Christmas ever because she is going to get a bike. This changes on Christmas Day when her sister wakes her up at six o'clock and she is given roller skates. It becomes the best Christmas again when she gets the bike. It continues because Minnie is grounded. It finally becomes the worst Christmas again when the writer crashes the bike.

Award 2 marks for answers that recognise some changes and give reasons.

Possible response:
- Before Christmas Day, the writer thinks this will be the best Christmas ever because she is going to get a bike. This changes on Christmas Day when she is given roller skates. It becomes the best Christmas again when she gets the bike. It finally becomes the worst Christmas again when the writer crashes the bike.

Award 1 mark for answers that recognise the overall change in attitude.
Possible response:
- The writer's attitude changes from it being the best Christmas at the start to the worst at the end.

14   **Award 1 mark** for: 1
- Hokkaido
- Honshu
- Shikoku
- Kyushu.

Do not penalise for spelling as long as the intention is clear.

15   **Award 1 mark** for: 1
- a hot, damp summer
- a cooler, drier winter.

16   **Award 1 mark** for mostly.   1

17   **a. Award 1 mark** for August.   1

    b. Award 1 mark for January.   1

18   **Award 2 marks** for answers that include the following and compare: 2
- the north: the winters are long and cold
- the Pacific coast: has milder winters with little snow.

Award 1 mark for answers that only contain one of the above or do not compare.

19   **Award 1 mark** for: 1
- electronics
- cars
- motorcycles.

Q	Answers	Marks
20	**Award 2 marks** for answers that include two of the following and compare: • Japan's rugby team is more successful than the football team. • The rugby team is the most successful in Asia. • The rugby team has won the Asia Five Nations competition six times. • The football team has reached the final stages of the FIFA World Cup. • The football team co-hosted the FIFA World Cup in 2002. **Award 1 mark** for answers that include two of the above but do not compare, or answers that include one of the above and compare.	2
21	**Award 2 marks** for a correct fact and a correct opinion. For example: • Fact: Japan's flag is the Rising Sun. • Opinion: its future seems bright. **Award 1 mark** for a correct fact or a correct opinion.	2
22	**Award 1 mark** for all four pairs matched correctly. There was a global recession. → 2009 Japan co-hosted the FIFA World Cup. → 2002 Japan was ranked third in the world's economies. → 2012 There was an earthquake and a tsunami. → 2011	1
23	**Award 1 mark** for In a geography textbook.	1
24	**Award 1 mark** for A snapshot of Japan.	1
25	**Award 1 mark** for morning.	1
26	**Award 1 mark** for grey.	1
27	**Award 1 mark** for a ship.	1
28	**Award 2 marks** for answers that give both an interpretation and an example. Possible responses: • The author shows that the sea was rough by saying that the 'ship was rolling in the ocean swell'. • He describes how the sea is making the boat move suddenly: 'jumping like an injured animal'. • The author describes the noises the boat is making to tell us that the sea is moving it: 'The rudder was banging to and fro' and 'the whole ship was creaking, groaning'. • Jim tells us that he is being thrown around in the boat so the sea must be rough: 'I had to cling on tight to the rope'. • The main character is being 'rolled about like a bottle' which tells us the boat is moving from side to side. **Award 1 mark** for answers that include either an explanation or an example but not both.	2
29	**Award 1 mark** for answers that suggest either of the following or similar: • The ship seemed as light as a bottle on the sea. • The ship had no control over itself.	1

Q	Answers	Marks
30	**Award I mark** for answers that show an understanding of the author's feeling of depression, fear or sadness.	I
31	**Award I mark** for any of the following quotations: • The men grumbled fiercely. • The very sight of the island seemed to have made them give up working. • If the behaviour of the men had been alarming in the boat, it became truly threatening when they had come back on board the *Hispaniola*. • They lay about the deck growling together in talk. • The slightest order was received with a black look and grudgingly and carelessly obeyed. • Mutiny, it was plain, hung over us like a thunder cloud.	I
32	**Award I mark** for except or words of similar meaning.	I
33	**Award I mark** for the island is an unhealthy place to go.	I
34	**Award I mark** for answers that indicate some sort of mutiny/rebellion will happen or that Long John will be overthrown.	I
35	**Award I mark** for rebellion.	I
36	**Award I mark** for to find the treasure.	I
37	**Award I mark** for answers that give a reason for the use of the first-person narrator. Possible responses: • To help us understand the character's point of view. • To make events seem more real. • To show us how the main character feels. • To make us feel as though the events are happening to us. • To make us feel that someone is telling a story of what happened to them. • To make us feel that the story is true.	I